The Tree House

by Daniel Barnes
illustrated by Dave Sullivan

Harcourt

Orlando   Boston   Dallas   Chicago   San Diego

Visit *The Learning Site!*

www.harcourtschool.com

We were all ready to start
our meeting. Then I heard
the sound of thunder.

"A storm is coming!" I announced. We climbed down the ladder and ran home. It's not safe to be in a tree house during a storm.

The next day the club
members all came back.
Everyone was sad. Everyone
looked glum.

"We don't have a tree house anymore!" cried Mark. "What are we going to do?"

"We all loved the tree house,"
I said. "We should rebuild it."
Even Mark started to smile.

"Yes. The tree is still good.
We can make the tree house
stronger this time."

Rosa and Al arrived with their mother. They had a bunch of tools.

Mark and Barb got the wood
from their old fruit stand.

Mrs. Martinez was a big help.
She did the cutting and
sawing. She showed us how
to hammer.

We all worked hard and learned a lot.

After two weeks, the new tree house was finished. It looked better than the old one.

We felt proud as we met in it for the first time.

Just before the meeting started, we heard the sound of thunder far away.

Everyone ran to my house this
time and watched. Would
the tree house be harmed?

After the storm, the tree house still looked great. We climbed the ladder and finally had our meeting!